Please, Do N Your Jelly beans

Please, do not drop
your jelly beans.

3

If you drop your jelly beans,
the baby will wake up
and cry like a fire alarm.

If the baby cries like a fire alarm, the firefighters will come to the house.

They will turn on their
big whooshing hoses.
You could get washed away
in the flood.

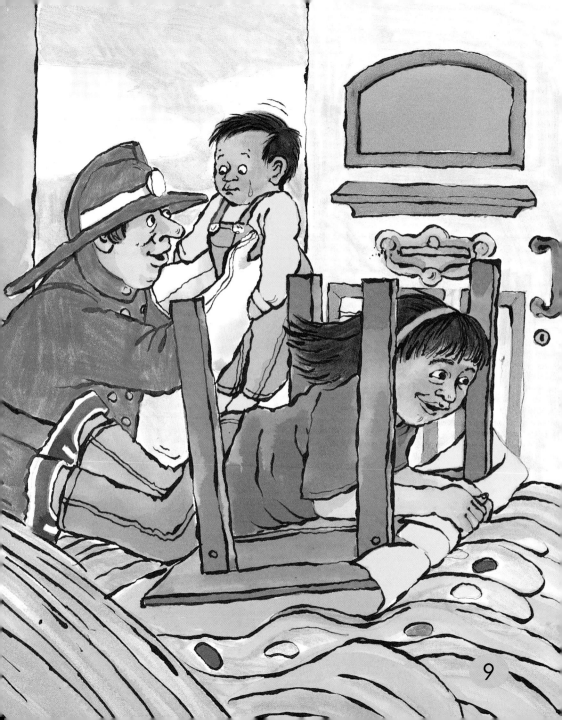

9

You might end up on the river.
If you end up on the river,
you could drift out
to the wild salt sea.

You could be attacked
by a shark
and a giant squid.

A pirate ship might chase you.
You might be caught in a huge storm.

Oh, the lightning!
Oh, the thunder!
Oh, the waves!

The pirate ship could be wrecked on some rocks. But you could be saved by a humpback whale.

The whale could take you
to the Arctic Ocean.
Then, before you could say
a word, the whale might
leave you on an iceberg.
You are not dressed
for icebergs.

So, please, please, please,
do not drop
your jelly beans.

Uh-oh, you did it!
You dropped
your jelly beans!